The Fas  e

When Karl's class went to the zoo, the teacher said,
"You must stay with your group.
Lions must stay with lions.
Tigers must stay with tigers.
Gazelles must stay with gazelles."

2

Karl was a gazelle.

3

"Let's go and see the monkeys!"
shouted Karl, and he ran on ahead.
"Wait for me," laughed the teacher.

"Let's go and see the bears!"
shouted Karl, and he ran on ahead.
"Wait for me," puffed the teacher.

"Let's go and see the seals!"
shouted Karl, and he ran on ahead.
"*Please* wait for me,"
panted the teacher.

SEALS

LIONS

FEEDING TIMES

OSTRICH

9

"Let's wait here for the teacher,"
said Karl.
"We can watch the seals being fed."

At last the teacher caught up.
"Isn't the zoo great!" said Karl.

14

Did you see the bears?

Did you see the seals?